# Best Loved

# NURSERY RHYMES

# AND

# SONGS

Editor
AUGUSTA BAKER
Coordinator of Children's Services
THE NEW YORK PUBLIC LIBRARY

Published By
PARENTS' MAGAZINE ENTERPRISES, INC.
For
PLAYMORE, INC.
New York, New York

*Best Loved*

# NURSERY
# RHYMES
### AND
# SONGS

• INCLUDING •

## MOTHER GOOSE
## SELECTIONS

1974 Edition

Originally Published as Vol. 1—Young Years Library

Copyright MCMLXIII

By

HOME LIBRARY PRESS

A Division Of Parents' Magazine Enterprises, Inc.

LIBRARY OF CONGRESS CATALOG NO. 63-12348

The Editor and Publisher wish to acknowledge with thanks the help and cooperation of the
following publishers for permission to reprint the stories listed below:

"The Sleighbells" from THE CHILDREN CAME RUNNING. Reprinted through the
courtesy of the United Nations Children's Fund (UNICEF)

"The Carol Singers" from THE CHILDREN CAME RUNNING. Reprinted through the
courtesy of the United Nations Children's Fund (UNICEF).

"Pipes and Drums" from THE CHILDREN CAME RUNNING. Reprinted through the
courtesy of the United Nations Children's Fund (UNICEF)

MANUFACTURED IN THE UNITED STATES OF AMERICA

# CONTENTS

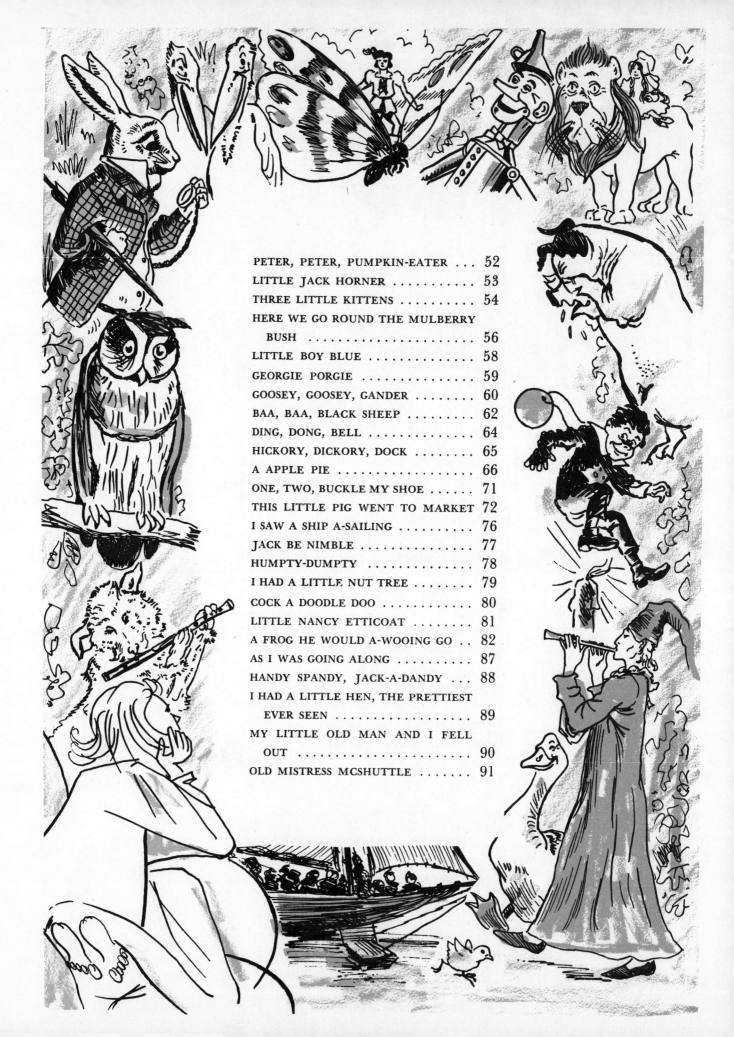

# Preface for Parents

All parents want to give their children the best of themselves, and their hopes for their children are the highest. They want them to grow fully and to have a rich, abundant life, and a good part of this stems from the family's relationships. There is a desire to do things together, and family reading is one way of satisfying this desire.

Accordingly, a family shares books at the earliest age of the first child. Parents who love books and who have shared their reading with each other will find themselves unconsciously speaking poetry and nursery rhymes, singing nursery songs to the small person who lies in his crib and listens. The child who has heard the songs from Walter Crane's *The Baby's Opera* is well prepared later for his pictures and for those of Kate Greenaway and Randolph Caldecott. The foundation is being made for this child's lifetime reading habits and tastes, and so it goes without saying that only the best is good enough for him.

Good taste can be developed, and so the standards for children's books must be high. A story or book must wear well artistically, and it is better to have a few of these outstanding books than many of the more modern yet mediocre titles conceived for the child. Give him the book that has been written with skill and a respect for words and style. All children read some books of doubtful merit, but the child with a good literary background can shed the ordinary and absorb the outstanding.

Sharing books should be a spontaneous, joyous activity and should be fun for both parents and children. It should not be a solemn duty motivated by a grim determination to make the child a little literary genius. There should be the contagion of real enthusiasm for reading so that the smallest child catches it from the lilt in the voice, and the reading child listens for the words, "This looks like a good book to read," or "Why don't you read this book and tell me whether or not you like it?" Bedtime is always a good time for the "reading period," but other times can be just as suitable. Mary Ellen Chase writes about the "reading periods" of her childhood held in the kitchen of the old Maine farmhouse. It had a large, sunny kitchen with red geraniums on its windows and a large black wood stove known as "The Rising Sun," the name in raised iron letters across the oven door. In *Recipe for a Magic Childhood,* Miss Chase writes, "My mother usually somehow managed, at eleven, to sit down for half an hour in the red rocking-chair by the window. She called this half hour her "respite," a word which early charmed me; and on days when no drafts were blowing across the floor (for even The Rising Sun was not always victorious over the worst of Maine weather) she would help us down from our Parnassus [the old secretary] and allow us to sit upon our red stools while, our cookies and milk consumed, she herself would read aloud to us. Here was the very doorsill to complete enchantment, for she was seemingly as lost as we in whatever she was reading. . . . There was always the excitement of our father's coming home at noon. . . . He was always interested, as he lifted us down from the secretary in what we had been reading; and . . . he would sometimes promise to go on that evening with an especial book, reading to us himself by the living-room fire while my mother, as avid a listener as we, would darn the countless socks and patch the red flannel underwear."

The exposure of a child to fine art and beauty cannot begin too early. It need not be presented stuffily as a lesson in art appreciation, but it can come about naturally through the child's handling of good picture books. These are the pictures that show both the familiar and the unfamiliar with beauty, humor, and vitality so that a child's sense of visual beauty is cultivated.

Then there are words to go along with the pictures, and they require a freshness and rhythm which makes their reading a listening delight. Parents should make every effort to read beautifully and to sing as sweetly as possible, for there is no better way of teaching the child who is learning to speak that words are musical. The child who is read to quickly understands the meaning and use of unfamiliar words. He shows a lively interest in these new words, enjoying the "feel" and sound of them as he repeats them over and over again. This is the beginning of interest and pleasure in language, and it leads to a discriminating and accurate use of it.

In the beginning, one reads and recites the familiar—the rhymes and jingles of Mother Goose, old nursery rhymes and songs,

12

for they are the natural heritage of the young. With every reading these old verses gain new vitality, and there is no need to change one word. For over two hundred years small children have chanted:

> *"Baa, Baa, black sheep,*
> *Have you any wool?*
> *Yes, sir, yes, sir,*
> *Three bags full;*
> *One for the master,*
> *And one for the dame,*
> *And one for the little boy*
> *Who lives down the lane."*

No one really knows who Mother Goose was or where the legend about her originated. The first book expressly made for children which contained traditional rhymes appeared in England in the early eighteenth century, and was called *A Little Book for Little Children.* Then followed *Tom Thumb's Pretty Song Book,* in two volumes, and *Mother Goose's Melody or Sonnets for the Cradle.* John Newbery is credited with being the publisher of the latter book and the first to use the name Mother Goose in connection with rhymes. Boston children hear about Dame Goose, and legend has it that she sang nursery rhymes to her grandchildren, and her son-in-law, Thomas Fleet, published them (1719) in a little book, *Songs for the Nursery; or Mother Goose's Melodies.* Unfortunately, no copy of this edition has ever been found to prove the truth of this legend. There is such a variety of subject matter and mood that the child is captivated by the fresh ideas. The rhythm and rhyme make him say, "Sing it again." He rocks his body, claps his hands, and taps his feet as Mother says,

> *"Hey! diddle, diddle,*
> *The cat and the fiddle,*
> *The cow jumped over the moon."*

The two-year-old develops his vocabulary as he repeats the rhymes, for they are simple to learn. Still another quality of these verses is their action. Mother Goose rides on her gander, Little Boy Blue blows his horn, and Humpty Dumpty falls down. The gay good humor of these verses sows the seed for the child's future sense of humor, a quality which the world truly needs.

The child moves from nursery rhymes to simple stories, but the quality of writing should still be high. In the eighteenth century, children read Isaac Watts' *Divine and Moral Songs for Children*. It was his intention to give children pleasure while making them aware of moral truths. This little guide to good moral conduct and other similar books were the main reading fare for English children; and then, one day, they received the first translation of the folk tales written by Charles Perrault. They were called *Histoires ou Contes du temps passé*, or, more familiarly, *Contes de ma Mère l'Oye* (Tales of Mother Goose). English children met Sleeping Beauty, Little Red Riding-Hood, and Cinderella. Today these are still favorite characters, but other simple stories have joined them in the nursery. Peter Rabbit and Jemima Puddleduck are characters in Beatrix Potter's miniature stories in which the animals are dressed in old-world costumes even while they retain all of the characteristics of small animals. Her stories and pictures are perfect in every detail. These simple nursery tales have a true theme which is developed through action and a recognizable plot and a combination of the familiar and imaginative, which gives the child a sense of extension beyond his own limited environment.

Folk and Fairy tales are soon encountered by the child. They are man's heritage, and they must be kept alive. Like the nursery rhymes, they are part of that great body of literature, anonymously created, known as folklore. It reveals man's efforts to explain and deal with the strange phenomena of nature, to understand and interpret the behavior of human beings and to express deep universal emotions. The Brothers Grimm collected the German tales; Peter Asbjörnsen and Jörgen Moe, as well as Sir George Dasent, collected the Norse tales. Andrew Lang and Joseph Jacobs were also well-known folklorists. Though these stories were not originally intended for children, they soon were claimed by them and adapted and retold for young readers. Though the youngest read the nursery tales and the simple folk tales, such as "Three Billy Goats Gruff," children reach their peak of interest in fairy tales when they are around eight and nine years old. The distinction between the old folk tale and the modern fairy tale is primarily one of authorship. The former came from the people, while the latter is the creative work of one imaginative mind. Hans Christian Andersen is usually credited with the first fairy tale. He began with skillful adaptations of traditional tales, but so creative was his genius that he turned them into literary gems and removed them entirely from the body of folk literature. Such stories as "Ugly Duckling" and "Real Princess" belong to

14

Hans Christian Andersen and not the folk. Perrault's stories, embellished though they were by a skilled writer, remained genuine folk tales. At times, the reading of these stories by children has been attacked by well-meaning adults who say it is "untruthful rubbish, contrary to what I am teaching my child is right." The truth of the matter is that people in folk tales behave pretty much as people do in real life. Annis Duff says, "Fairy tales do not 'condone' behavior that is contrary to ethical principle. They simply recognize the fact that it occurs. The mother who was so flustered about the possible detriment to her children of reading fairy tales overlooked the fact that she herself had read them and still retained a well-developed sense of right and wrong.

Children also enjoy the fables though they are better understood by the older children because of their intellectual quality as compared with the simple folk tales. They make abstract ideas objective enough to be understood with their maxims, adages, and brief moralizings. One rarely sympathizes with the fable creature, for he is an impersonal exemplification of virtue or folly. Younger children will enjoy the few fables which have strong story appeal or obvious humor, such as "The Town Mouse and the Country Mouse," "The Hare and The Tortoise," or "Dog in the Manger." The English-speaking child is familiar with Aesop's fables while French children associate fables with Jean de la Fontaine. Aesop is said to have lived between 620 and 560 B.C. and to have been a Greek slave from Ethiopia. La Fontaine (1621–1695) was a poet, a member of the Royal Academy, and a contemporary of Perrault. He drew upon many sources for his fables, including Aesop and the Indian fables of Bidpai. The oldest and largest body of fables is the collection of Jatakas, which formed a part of ancient Buddhist literature. Since the maxims of these great fablers and fabulists have passed into our thinking and our language, every child should be introduced to them.

It is never too soon to speak poetry to a child. Mother Goose should keep company with Shakespeare, William Blake, and Christina Rossetti. Nonsense makers, such as Edward Lear and Lewis Carroll, should be included, for a good laugh is priceless. Starting with Mother Goose, the family moves from the little verse, used to point up an occasion or provoke laughter, to the real poem which touches upon the why and how of being. Poetry is essential to the full development of the child, and, if he stores up beauty and magnificence, there is less room for the ugly and mediocre. Poetry should be shared by the family and, if possible, recited from memory rather than read. If it is not recited, it should be read with affection and feeling. Reading a poem aloud catches elements which are missed when it is read silently. The melody and movement of oral interpretation suggest action and establish mood. Use poetry with children for their enjoyment, for stimulation and relaxation, for quiet reassurance. Be not concerned with the meaning of a poem or its difficulty because of the child's limited experience, for a great poem speaks to the emotions rather than to the intellect. A child may learn a poem for its beautiful words and imagery only to realize its deeper meaning years later. The child who is introduced to poetry in his infancy will love and appreciate it throughout his life. The selections in this volume are an introduction, a taste of the great body of poetry and it is hoped that this taste will lead to a long and exciting relationship between the child and the poem.

The selections here of *Nursery Rhymes and Songs* were made by people who have devoted many years to books and children. The editors hope that these carefully made selections will serve as a springboard to further exploration of children's literature. Here is a starting point for the parents who are a little unsure of their own knowledge and judgment.

A.B.

16

# NURSERY
# RHYMES

# OLD MOTHER HUBBARD

Old Mother Hubbard
     Went to the cupboard,
To get her poor dog a bone,
     But when she got there
The cupboard was bare,
     And so the poor dog had none.

She went to the baker's
    To buy him some bread,
But when she came back
    The poor dog was dead.

She went to the joiner's
    To buy him a coffin,
But when she came back
    The poor dog was laughing.

She went to the fishmonger's
    To buy him some fish,
And when she came back
    He was licking the dish.

She went to the ale-house
    To get him some beer,
But when she came back
    The dog sat in a chair.

She took a clean dish
    To get him some tripe,
But when she came back
    He was smoking his pipe.

She went to the barber's
    To buy him a wig,
But when she came back
    He was dancing a jig.

She went to the tavern
    For white wine and red,
But when she came back
    The dog stood on his head.

She went to the hatter's
    To buy him a hat,
But when she came back
    He was feeding the cat.

She went to the tailor's
    To buy him a coat,
But when she came back
    He was riding a goat.

She went to the fruiterer's
    To buy him some fruit,
But when she came back
    He was playing the flute.

She went to the cobbler's
    To buy him some shoes,
But when she came back
    He was reading the news.

21

She went to the seamstress
    To buy him some linen,
But when she came back
    The dog was spinning.

She went to the hosier's
    To buy him some hose,
But when she came back
    He was dressed in his clothes.

The dame made a curtsy,
    The dog made a bow,
The dame said, "Your servant,"
    The dog said, "Bow, wow."

# THE MAN
# IN THE
# MOON

The man in the moon,
Came down too soon,
To inquire his way
    to Norwich:
He went by the south,
And burnt his mouth
With eating cold
        plum-porridge.

# LITTLE BO-PEEP

Little Bo-peep has lost her sheep,
    And can't tell where to find them;
Leave them alone, and they'll come home,
    And bring their tails behind them.

Little Bo-peep fell fast asleep,
　　And dreamt she heard them bleating;
And when she awoke, she found it a joke,
　　For they still were all fleeting.

Then up she took her little crook,
　　Determin'd for to find them;
She found them indeed, but it made her heart bleed,
　　For they'd left all their tails behind 'em.

# HUSH-A-BYE
# BABY

Hush-a-bye, baby,
    on the tree top,
When the wind blows,
    the cradle will rock;
When the bough breaks,
    the cradle will fall
Down will come baby,
    bough, cradle, and all.

# LITTLE
# MISS
# MUFFETT

Little Miss Muffett
    She sat on a tuffett,
Eating of curds and whey;

There came a black spider,
    And sat down beside her,
Which frightened Miss Muffett away.

# THERE WAS AN OLD WOMAN WHO LIVED IN A SHOE

There was an old woman
                who lived in a shoe;
She had so many children
                she didn't know what to do.

She gave them some broth
                without any bread;
She whipped them all soundly,
                and put them to bed.

# BYE, BABY

# BUNTING

Bye, Baby bunting,
      Daddy's gone a-hunting,
To get a little
      rabbit skin
To wrap a baby
      bunting in.

# SING A
# SONG OF SIXPENCE

Sing a song of sixpence,
    A pocket full of rye;
Four and twenty blackbirds
    Baked in a pie.

When the pie was opened,
    The birds began to sing;
Was not that a dainty dish,
    To set before the king?

The king was in his counting-house
        Counting out his money;
The queen was in the parlor
        Eating bread and honey;

The maid was in the garden
        Hanging out the clothes,
There came a little blackbird,
        And snapped off her nose.

# HOW MANY MILES

# TO BABYLON?

How many miles is it to Babylon?
        Threescore miles and ten.
Can I get there by candle-light?
        Yes, and back again!
If your heels are nimble and light,
        You may get there by candle-light.

# MISTRESS MARY

# QUITE CONTRARY

Mistress Mary,
　　quite contrary,
How does your
　　garden grow?
With cockle-shells,
　　and silver bells,
And pretty maids
　　all in a row.

# JACK
# AND
# JILL

Jack and Jill
        went up the hill,
To fetch
        a pail of water;

Jack fell down
        and broke his crown
And Jill came
        tumbling after.

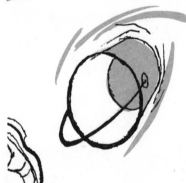

Up Jack got
        and home did trot
As fast as
        he could caper;
To Old Dame Dob
        Who patched his knob
With vinegar
        and brown paper.

# HEY! DIDDLE, DIDDLE

Hey! diddle, diddle!
    The cat and the fiddle.
The cow jumped over the moon;

    The little dog laughed
    To see such sport,
And the dish ran away with the spoon.

# SIMPLE SIMON

Simple Simon met a pieman,
  Going to the fair;
Says Simple Simon to the pieman,
  "Let me taste your ware."

Says the pieman to Simple Simon,
    "Show me first your penny."
Says Simple Simon to the pieman,
    "Indeed I have not any."

Simple Simon went a-fishing
    For to catch a whale;
All the water he could find
    Was in his mother's pail!

Simple Simon went to look
    If plums grew on a thistle;
He pricked his fingers very much,
    Which made poor Simon whistle.

He went to catch a dicky bird,
       And thought he could not fail,
Because he had a little salt,
       To put upon its tail.

He went for water with a sieve,
       But soon it all ran through;
And now poor Simple Simon
       Bids you all adieu.

# AS I WAS GOING TO ST. IVES

As I was going to St. Ives,
I met a man with seven wives,
Every wife had seven sacks,
Every sack had seven cats,
Every cat had seven kits:
Kits, cats, sacks, and wives,
How many were there going to St. Ives?

# HICKETY, PICKETY

## MY BLACK HEN

Hickety, pickety, my black hen,
      She lays eggs for gentlemen;
Gentlemen come every day,
      To see what my black hen doth lay.

# JACK SPRAT

Jack Sprat could eat no fat,
His wife could eat no lean,
And so between them both, you see,
They licked the platter clean.

# RIDE A COCK-HORSE

Ride a cock-horse
      to Banbury Cross,
To see an old lady
      upon a white horse,
Rings on her fingers,
      and bells on her toes,
She shall have music
      wherever she goes.

# PUSSY-CAT, PUSSY-CAT
# WHERE HAVE YOU BEEN?

"Pussy-cat, Pussy-cat,
  where have you been?"
"I've been to London, to see the Queen!"
"Pussy-cat, Pussy-cat,
  what did you there?"
"I frightened a little mouse under the chair!"

# WEE WILLIE WINKIE

Wee Willie Winkie runs
        through the town,
Upstairs and downstairs,
        in his nightgown,
Rapping at the window,
        crying through the lock,
"Are the children in their beds?
        now it's eight o'clock."

# THE QUEEN OF HEARTS

The queen of hearts,
She made some tarts,
All on a summer's day;

The knave of hearts,
        He stole those tarts,
And with them ran away:

The king of hearts
        Called for those tarts,
And beat the knave full sore;

The knave of hearts
        Brought back those tarts,
And said he'd ne'er steal more.

# TOM, TOM

# THE PIPER'S SON

Tom, Tom, the piper's son,
Stole a pig and away he run;
The pig was eat,
And Tom was beat,
And Tom went howling
down the street.

# SEE-SAW
## MARGERY
### DAW

See-Saw, Margery Daw,
Jenny shall have
          a new master;
And she shall have
          but a penny a day,
Because she can't
          work any faster.

# OLD KING COLE

Old King Cole
Was a merry old soul,
And a merry old soul was he;

He called for his pipe,
And he called for his bowl,
And he called for his fiddlers three.

And every fiddler he had a fine fiddle,
      And a very fine fiddle had he;
"Twee tweedle dee, tweedle dee,"
      went the fiddlers.
Oh, there's none so rare,
      As can compare
With King Cole and his fiddlers three.

# PETER, PETER

## PUMPKIN-EATER

Peter, Peter, pumpkin-eater,
    Had a wife, and couldn't keep her;
He put her in a pumpkin-shell,
    And there he kept her very well.

# LITTLE JACK HORNER

Little Jack Horner
    sat in the corner,
        Eating a Christmas pie;
He put in his thumb,
    and he took out a plum,
        And said, "What a good boy am I!"

# THREE LITTLE KITTENS

Three little kittens
    lost their mittens,
And they began to cry.
    "O mother dear,
    We very much fear
    That we have lost
      our mittens."

"Lost your mittens!
    You naughty kittens!
Then you shall have no pie."
    "Mee-ow, mee-ow, mee-ow."
"No, you shall have no pie."
"Mee-ow,

      mee-ow,

        mee-ow."

The three little kittens
    found their
    mittens,
And they began to cry,
    "O mother dear,
    See here, see here
See! we have found
    our mittens."

"Put on your mittens,
    You silly kittens,
And you may have some pie."
    "Purr-r, purr-r, purr-r,
Oh, let us have the pie.
    Purr-r, purr-r, purr-r."

The three little kittens
      put on their mittens,
And soon ate up the pie;
   "O mother dear,
   We greatly fear
   That we have soil'd
      our mittens."

"Soiled your mittens!
   You naughty kittens!"
Then they began to sigh,
   "Mee-ow, mee-ow,
            mee-ow."
Then they began to sigh,
"Mee-ow,

      mee-ow,

            mee-ow."

The three little kittens
      washed their
         mittens,
And hung them out
      to dry;
   "O mother dear,
   Do you not hear,
That we have washed
      our mittens?"

"Washed your mittens!
   Oh, you're good kittens.
But I smell a rat close by!"
   "Hush, hush! mee-ow, mee-ow!
We smell a rat close by!
Mee-ow,

      mee-ow,

            mee-ow!"

*Eliza Lee Follen*

# HERE WE GO ROUND

## THE MULBERRY BUSH

Here we go round the mulberry bush,
        The mulberry bush, the mulberry bush;
Here we go round the mulberry bush,
        On a cold and frosty morning!

This is the way we wash our clothes,
        Wash our clothes, wash our clothes;
This is the way we wash our clothes,
        On a cold and frosty morning!

This is the way we dry our clothes,
      Dry our clothes, dry our clothes;
This is the way we dry our clothes,
      On a cold and frosty morning!

This is the way we mend our shoes,
      Mend our shoes, mend our shoes;
This is the way we mend our shoes,
      On a cold and frosty morning!

This is the way the ladies walk,
      Ladies walk, ladies walk;
This is the way the ladies walk,
      On a cold and frosty morning!

This is the way the gentlemen walk,
      Gentlemen walk, gentlemen walk;
This is the way the gentlemen walk,
      On a cold and frosty morning!

# LITTLE BOY BLUE

Little boy blue, come blow your horn,
The sheep's in the meadow,
the cow's in the corn.
Where's the boy that looks after
the sheep?
He's under the haycock,
fast asleep.

Will you wake him? No, not I;
For if I do, he'll be sure to cry.

58

# GEORGIE PORGIE

Georgie Porgie, pudding and pie,
    Kissed the girls and made them cry.
When the girls came out to play,
    Georgie Porgie ran away.

# GOOSEY GOOSEY GANDER

Goosey, goosey, gander,
  Who stands yonder?
Little Betsey Baker;
  Take her up, and shake her.

Goosey, goosey, gander,
  Where shall I wander?
Upstairs, downstairs,
  And in my lady's chamber.

There I met an old man
　　That would not say his prayers
I took him by the left leg,
　　And threw him downstairs.

# BAA, BAA
## BLACK SHEEP

Baa, baa, black sheep,
        Have you any wool?
Yes, sir, yes, sir,
        Three bags full.

One for my master,
     And one for my dame,
And one for the little boy
     Who lives in the lane.

# DING, DONG, BELL

Ding, dong bell,
Pussy's in the well!
Who put her in?
Little Tommy Lin.
Who pulled her out?
Little
    Johnny
      Stout.

What a naughty boy
    was that
To drown the poor,
    poor pussy-cat
Who never did him
    any harm,
But killed the mice
    in his father's barn.

64

# HICKORY
## DICKORY
## DOCK

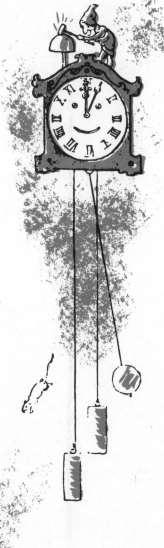

Hickory,
　　dickory,
　　　　dock,
The mouse ran up
　　the clock;
The clock struck
　　　　one,
And down he run,
Hickory,
　　dickory,
　　　　dock,

# A

WAS AN APPLE PIE

# B

BIT IT

# C

CUT IT

# D

DEALT IT

E

F

G

H

**EAT IT**

**FOUGHT FOR IT**

**GOT IT**

**HAD IT**

# I J & K L M

## JUMPED FOR IT

## KNELT FOR IT

## LONGED FOR IT

## MOURNED FOR IT

N

O

P

Q

NODDED AT IT

OPENED IT

PEEPED IN IT

QUARTERED IT

69

# R

## RAN FOR IT

# S

## SANG FOR IT

# T

## TOOK IT

# U V W
# X Y Z

### ALL HAD A LARGE SLICE
### AND WENT OFF TO
### BED

# ONE, TWO, BUCKLE MY SHOE

One, two,
Buckle my shoe;

Three, four,
Shut the door;

Five, six,
Pick up sticks;

Seven, eight,
Lay them straight;

Nine, ten,
A good fat hen;

Eleven, twelve,
Who will delve?

Thirteen, fourteen,
Maids a-courting;

Fifteen, sixteen,
Maids a-kissing;

Seventeen, eighteen,
Maids a-waiting;

Nineteen, twenty,
My stomach's empty
Pray, dame, give me some supper.

# THIS LITTLE PIG
# WENT TO MARKET

This little pig
went to market;

This little pig
stayed at home;

This little pig
    had roast beef;

This little pig
    had none;

This little pig
        said, "Wee, wee!
I can't find my way

# home."

# I SAW A
# SHIP A-SAILING

I saw a ship a-sailing,
    A-sailing on the sea;
And, oh! it was all laden
    With pretty things for thee!

There were comfits in the cabin,
      And apples in the hold;
The sails were made of silk,
      And the masts were made of gold.

The four-and-twenty sailors
      That stood between the decks
Were four-and-twenty white mice,
      With chains about their necks.

The captain was a duck,
      With a packet on his back;
And when the ship began to move,
      The captain said, "Quack! quack!"

# JACK

# BE NIMBLE

Jack be nimble,
      And Jack be quick;
And Jack jump over
      The candlestick.

# HUMPTY DUMPTY

Humpty Dumpty sat on a wall,
    Humpty Dumpty had a great fall;
All the King's horses and all the King's men
    Couldn't put Humpty Dumpty together
    again.

# I HAD A
# LITTLE NUT TREE

I had a little nut-tree;
  nothing would it bear
But a silver nutmeg
  and a golden pear;
The King of Spain's daughter
  came to visit me
And all was because of my
  little nut-tree.

I skipped over water,
  I danced over sea,
And all the birds in the air
  couldn't catch me.

# COCK A DOODLE DOO

Cock a doodle doo!
      My dame has lost her shoe;
My master's lost his fiddling stick,
      And don't know what to do.

Cock a doodle doo!
      What is my dame to do?
Till master finds his fiddling stick,
      She'll dance without her shoe.

Cock a doodle doo!
      My dame has found her shoe,
And master's found his fiddling stick,
      Sing doodle doodle do!

Cock a doodle doo!
      My dame will dance with you,
While master fiddles his fiddling stick,
      For dame and doodle doo.

# LITTLE
# NANCY
# ETTICOAT

Little Nancy Etticoat,
      In a white petticoat,
And a red nose;
      The longer she stands,
The shorter she grows.

# A FROG HE WOULD
# A-WOOING GO

A FROG he would a-wooing go,
    Heighho, says Rowley!
Whether his Mother would let him or no.
    With a rowley-powley, gammon and spinach,
    Heighho, says Anthony Rowley!

So off he set with his opera hat,
    Heighho, says Rowley!
And on his way he met with a Rat.
    With a rowley-powley, gammon and spinach,
    Heighho, says Anthony Rowley!

"Pray, Mister Rat, will you go with me?"
   Heighho, says Rowley!
"Pretty Miss Mousey for to see?"
   With a rowley-powley, gammon and spinach,
   Heighho, says Anthony Rowley!


Now they soon arrived at Mousey's Hall,
   Heighho, says Rowley!
And gave a loud knock, and gave a loud call.
   With a rowley-powley, gammon and spinach,
   Heighho, says Anthony Rowley!

"Pray, Miss Mousey, are you within?"
   Heighho, says Rowley!
"Oh yes, kind Sirs, I'm sitting to spin."
   With a rowley-powley, gammon and spinach,
   Heighho, says Anthony Rowley!

"Pray, Miss Mousey, will you give us some beer?"
    Heighho, says Rowley!
"For Froggy and I are fond of good cheer."
    With a rowley-powley, gammon and spinach,
    Heighho, says Anthony Rowley!

"Pray Mister Frog, will you give us a song?"
    Heighho, says Rowley!
"But let it be something that's not very long."
    With a rowley-powley, gammon and spinach,
    Heighho, says Anthony Rowley!

"Indeed Miss Mouse," replied Mister Frog,
    Heighho, says Rowley!
"A cold has made me as hoarse as a Hog."
    With a rowley-powley, gammon and spinach,
    Heighho, says Anthony Rowley!

"Since you have caught cold," Miss Mousey said,
    Heighho, says Rowley!
"I'll sing you a song that I have just made."
    With a rowley-powley, gammon and spinach,
    Heighho, says Anthony Rowley!

But while they were all thus a merry-making,
    Heighho, says Rowley!
A cat and her kittens came tumbling in.
    With a rowley-powley, gammon and spinach,
    Heighho, says Anthony Rowley!

The Cat she seized the Rat by the crown;
    Heighho, says Rowley!
The kittens they pulled the little Mouse down.
    With a rowley-powley, gammon and spinach,
    Heighho, says Anthony Rowley!

This put Mister Frog in a terrible fright;
    Heighho, says Rowley!
He took up his hat, and he wished them good night.
    With a rowley-powley, gammon and spinach,
    Heighho, says Anthony Rowley!

But as Froggy was crossing over a silvery brook,
    Heighho, says Rowley!
A lily-white duck came and gobbled him up.
    With a rowley-powley, gammon and spinach,
    Heighho, says Anthony Rowley!

So there was an end of one, two and three,
    Heighho, says Rowley!
The Rat, the Mouse, and the little Frog-ee
    With a rowley-powley, gammon and spinach,
    Heighho, says Anthony Rowley!

# AS I WAS GOING ALONG

As I was going along, long, long,
    A singing a comical song, song, song,
The lane that I went was so long, long, long,
    And the song that I sung was as long, long, long,
And so I went singing along.

# HANDY SPANDY
# JACK-A-DANDY

Handy Spandy, Jack-a-dandy,
    Loved plum-cake and sugar-candy;
He bought some at a grocer's shop,
    And out he came, hop, hop, hop.

# I HAD A LITTLE HEN
# THE PRETTIEST
# EVER SEEN

I had a little hen, the prettiest ever seen;
      She washed me the dishes, and kept the house
          clean;
She went to the mill to fetch me some flour;
      She brought it home in less than an hour;
She baked me my bread, she brewed me my ale;
      She sat by the fire, and told many a fine tale.

# MY LITTLE OLD MAN
# AND I FELL OUT

My little old man and I fell out;
      I'll tell you what 'twas all about:
I had money, and he had none,
      And that's the way the row begun.

# OLD MISTRESS MCSHUTTLE

Old mistress McShuttle
Lived in a coal-scuttle,
Along with her dog and her cat;
What they ate I can't tell,
But 'tis known very well,
That none of the party were fat.

# ROBIN AND RICHARD

Robin and Richard were two pretty men;
      They lay in bed till the clock struck ten;
Then up starts Robin and 'looks at the sky,
      Oh! Brother Richard, the sun's very high.

The bull's in the barn threshing the corn,
      The cock's on the rooftop blowing his horn,
The cat's at the fire frying of fish,
      The dog's in the pantry breaking his dish.

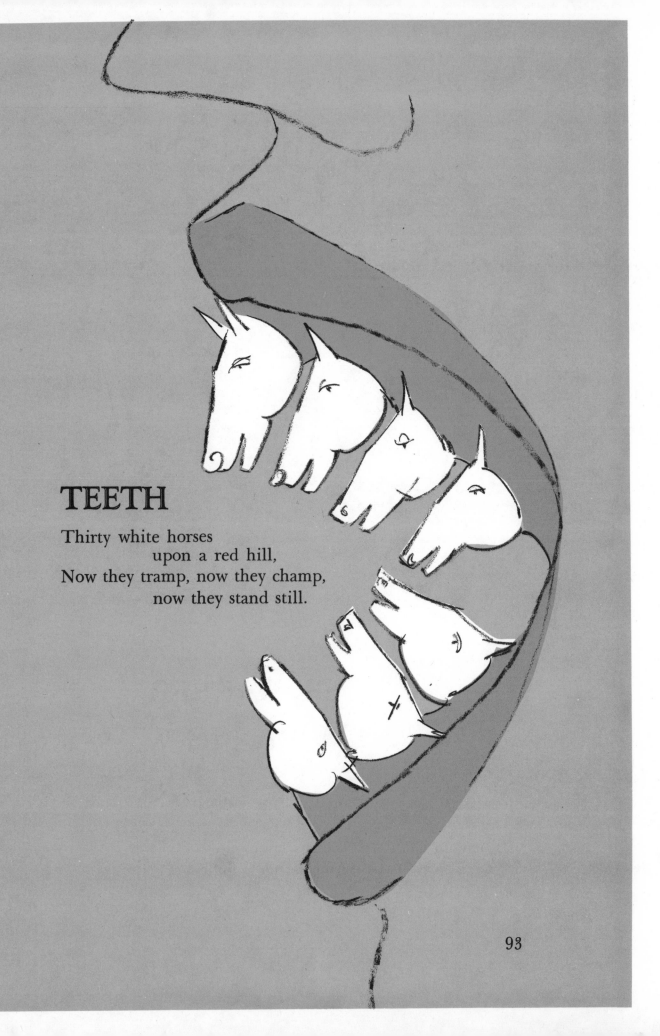

# TEETH

Thirty white horses
        upon a red hill,
Now they tramp, now they champ,
        now they stand still.

# BARBER, BARBER
## SHAVE A PIG

Barber, barber, shave a pig;
How many hairs will make a wig?
"Four-and-twenty, that's enough."
Give the barber a pinch of snuff.

# LITTLE JOHN
# JIGGY JAG

Little John Jiggy Jag,
He rode a penny nag,
  And went to Wigan to woo:
When he came to a beck,
He fell and broke his neck,—
  Johnny, how dost thou now?

I made him a hat,
Of my coat-lap,
  And stockings of pearly blue.
A hat and a feather,
To keep out cold weather;
  So, Johnny, how dost thou now?

# SEE-SAW SACRADOWN

See-saw sacradown,
      Which is the way to London Town?
One foot up and the other down,
      And that is the way to London Town.

# THREE WISE MEN
# OF GOTHAM

Three wise men of Gotham
    Went to sea in a bowl:
And if the bowl had been stronger,
    My song would have been longer.

# CROSS PATCH
# DRAW THE LATCH

Cross patch,
  Draw the latch,
Sit by the fire and spin;
  Take a cup,
  And drink it up,
Then call your neighbors in.

# JOHNNY CROW'S GARDEN

Johnny Crow
Would dig and sow
Till he made a little Garden.

And the Lion
Had a green and yellow Tie on
In Johnny Crow's Garden !

And the Rat
Wore a Feather in his Hat

But the Bear
Had nothing to wear
In Johnny Crow's Garden.

So the Ape
Took his Measure with a Tape
In Johnny Crow's Garden.

Then the Crane
Was caught in the Rain
In Johnny Crow's Garden.

And the Beaver
Was afraid he had a Fever

But the Goat
Said :
" It's nothing but his Throat ! "
In Johnny Crow's Garden.

And the Pig
Danced a Jig
In Johnny Crow's Garden.

Then the Stork
Gave a Philosophic Talk
Till the Hippopotami
Said : "Ask no further 'What am I?'"

While the Elephant
Said something quite irrelevant
In Johnny Crow's Garden.

And the Goose—
Well,
the Goose *was* a Goose
In Johnny Crow's Garden.

And the Mouse
Built himself a little House
Where the Cat
Sat down beside the Mat
In Johnny Crow's Garden.

And the Whale
Told a very long Tale
In Johnny Crow's Garden.

And the Owl
Was a funny old Fowl

And the Fox
Put them all in the Stocks
In Johnny Crow's Garden.

But Johnny Crow
He let them go

And they all sat down
to their dinner in a row
In Johnny Crow's Garden.

# LITTLE MAID, PRETTY MAID
# WHITHER GOEST THOU?

"Little maid, pretty maid, whither goest thou?"
      "Down in the meadow to milk my cow."
"Shall I go with thee?" "No, not now;
      When I send for thee, then come thou."

# THE FARMER'S BOY

When I was a farmer, a Farmer's Boy,
I used to keep my master's HORSES,
With a GEE-wo here, and a GEE-wo there,
And here a GEE, and there a GEE,
And everywhere a GEE;
Says I,  My pretty lass, will you come to the banks
of the Aire oh?

When I was a farmer, a Farmer's Boy,
I used to keep my master's LAMBS,
With a BAA-BAA here, and a BAA-BAA there,
And here a BAA, and there a BAA,
And everywhere a BAA;
With a GEE-WO here, and a GEE-WO there,
And here a GEE, and there a GEE,
And everywhere a GEE;
Says I,   My pretty lass, will you come to the banks
of the Aire oh?

When I was a farmer, a Farmer's Boy,
I used to keep my master's HENS,

With a CHUCK-CHUCK here, and a CHUCK-CHUCK
    there,
    And here a CHUCK, and there a CHUCK,
    And everywhere a CHUCK;

With a BAA-BAA here, and a BAA-BAA there,
    And here a BAA, and there a BAA,
    And everywhere a BAA;

With a GEE-WO here, and a GEE-WO there,
      &c.,     &c.,     &c.

Says I,     My pretty lass, will you come to the banks
    of the Aire oh?

When I was a farmer, a Farmer's Boy,

118

I used to keep my master's PIGS,
With a GRUNT-GRUNT here, and a GRUNT-GRUNT
        there,
    And here a GRUNT, and there a GRUNT,
    And everywhere a GRUNT;
With a CHUCK-CHUCK here, and a CHUCK-CHUCK
        there,
    And here a CHUCK, and there a CHUCK,
    And everywhere a CHUCK;
With a BAA-BAA here, and a BAA-BAA there,
        &c.,        &c.,        &c.
With a GEE-WO here, and a GEE-WO there,
        &c.,        &c.,        &c.

Says I,     My pretty lass, will you come to the banks
            of the Aire oh?

            When I was a farmer, a Farmer's Boy,
              I used to keep my master's DUCKS,
            With a QUACK-QUACK here, and a QUACK-QUACK
                there,
                And here a QUACK, and there a QUACK,
                And everywhere a QUACK;
            With a GRUNT-GRUNT here, and a GRUNT-GRUNT
                there,
                        &c.,      &c.,      &c.
            With a CHUCK-CHUCK here, &c.
            With a BAA-BAA here, &c.
            With a GEE-WO here, &c.

Says I,     My pretty lass, will you come to the banks
            of the Aire oh?

When I was a farmer, a Farmer's Boy,
   I used to keep my master's DOGS,
With a BOW-BOW here, and a Bow-wow there,
   And here a Bow, and there a Wow,
   And everywhere a Wow;
With a QUACK-QUACK here, and a QUACK-QUACK
   there,
        &c.,      &c.,      &c.
With a GRUNT-GRUNT here, &c.
With a CHUCK-CHUCK here, &c.
With a BAA-BAA here, &c.
With a GEE-WO here, &c.
Says I,     My pretty lass, will you come to the banks
        of the Aire oh?
When I was a farmer, a Farmer's Boy,

I used to keep my master's CHILDREN,
With a SHOUTING here, and a POUTING there,
And here a SHOUT, and there a POUT,
And everywhere a SHOUT;
With a BOW-BOW here, and a BOW-WOW there,
&c.,     &c.,     &c.
With a QUACK-QUACK here, &c.
With a GRUNT-GRUNT here, &c.
With a CHUCK-CHUCK here, &c.
With a BAA-BAA here, &c.
With a GEE-WO here, &c.

Says I,     My pretty lass, will you come to the banks
of the Aire oh?

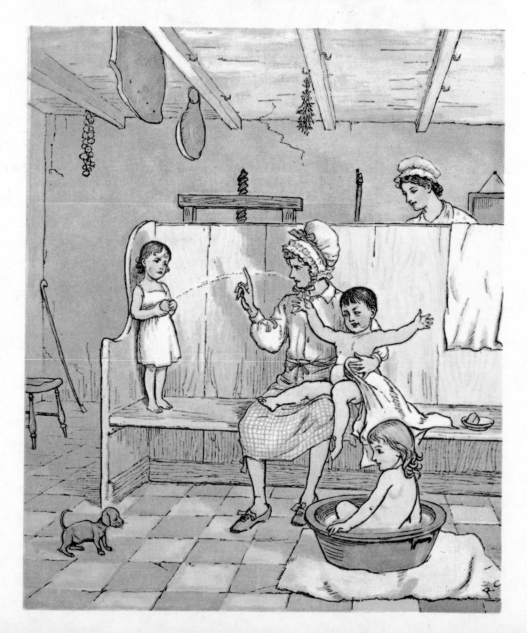

When I was a farmer, a Farmer's Boy,
  I used to keep my master's TURKEYS,
With a GOBBLE-GOBBLE here, and a GOBBLE-
    GOBBLE there,
  And here a GOBBLE, and there a GOBBLE;
  And everywhere a GOBBLE;
With a SHOUTING here, and a POUTING there,
      &c.,    &c.,    &c.

With a BOW-WOW here, &c.
With a QUACK-QUACK here, &c.
With a GRUNT-GRUNT here, &c.
With a CHUCK-CHUCK here, &c.
With a BAA-BAA here, &c.
With a GEE-WO here, &c.

Says I,    My pretty lass, will you come to the banks
      of the Aire oh?

# THE LION AND
# THE UNICORN

The Lion and the Unicorn
  Were fighting for the Crown;
The Lion beat the Unicorn
  All round about the town.

Some gave them white bread,
  And some gave them brown;
Some gave them plum-cake,
  And sent them out of town.

# THE SLEIGHBELLS

Merrily, merrily go the bells,
And merrily, too, go we,
Through the dark woods and past the church
Carrying our Christmas tree.

We sing to the song of the bells,
And the old horse turns one ear,
While all the forest holds its breath
Our carolling to hear.

Our carolling to hear
With Christ's birth drawing near
And every star a Christmas star
Above that Child so dear.

*Elizabeth Coatsworth*

# PIPES AND DRUMS

Sometimes as the air grows cooler
And the leaves stir just a little,
When the dust is soft and golden,
And the roofs seem bright and brittle,
And the camels long for home,
And the dogs forget to bark,
Come the three old street musicians
Making music in the park.

One musician (he has whiskers)
Taps upon a little drum,
One musician, in a turban
Plays a horn for all who come,
And the third plays on the cymbals,
Lightly strikes them tink tank tink.
(He is just a trifle bow-legged
And he wears a coat of pink.)

*Elizabeth Coatsworth*

127

# THE CAROL SINGERS

The church is lighted
The snow is falling,
The carol singers stand outside.
They hold their music,
Loudly singing
(Their mouths are open ever so wide!)

The trees are covered
With snow like specters,
And snowflakes dot the shining night,
While the sky itself
Is hung with baubles—
A moon and six stars (if I've counted them right!)

*Elizabeth Coatsworth*

# BOW, WOW, WOW

Bow, wow, wow,
        Whose dog art thou?
"Little Tom Tinker's dog,
        Bow, wow, wow."

# THERE WAS
# A LITTLE GIRL
# AND SHE
# HAD A LITTLE CURL

There was a little girl,
And she had a little curl,
That hung in the middle of her forehead;
When she was good,
She was very, very good,
But when she was bad she was horrid.

# THERE WAS AN OLD WOMAN TOSSED UP IN A BASKET

There was an old woman tossed up in a basket
      Nineteen times as high as the moon;
Where she was going I couldn't but ask her,
      For in her hand she carried a broom.

"Old woman, old woman, old woman," quoth I,
      "O whither, O whither, O whither, so high?"
"To brush the cobwebs off the sky!"
      "Shall I go with thee?"
"Ay, by-and-by."

131

# THE NORTH WIND
# DOTH BLOW

The north wind doth blow,
      And we shall have snow,
And what will the robin do then,
      Poor thing?

He'll sit in a barn,
      And keep himself warm,
And hide his head under his wing,
      Poor thing!

# LITTLE POLLY FLINDERS

Little Polly Flinders
      Sat among the cinders,
Warming her pretty little toes.
      Her mother came and caught her,
And whipped her little daughter
      For spoiling her nice new clothes.

# I HAD A LITTLE PONY

I had a little pony,
    His name was Dapple-grey;
I lent him to a lady,
    To ride a mile away.
She whipped him, she slashed him,
    She rode him through the mire;
I would not lend my pony now
    For all the lady's hire.

ON
YONDER
HILL
THERE
STANDS
A
TREE

On yonder hill there stands a tree;
    Tree on the hill, and the hill stood still.

And on the tree there was a branch;
    Branch on the tree, tree on the hill, and the hill
        stood still.

And on the branch there was a nest:
> Nest on the branch, branch on the tree, tree on
> the hill, and the hill stood still.

And in the nest there was an egg:
> Egg in the nest, nest on the branch, branch on
> the tree, tree on the hill, and the hill
> stood still.

And in the egg there was a bird;
      Bird in the egg, egg in the nest, nest on the
      branch, branch on the tree, tree on
      the hill, and the hill stood still.

And on the bird there was a feather;
      Feather on the bird, bird in the egg, egg in the
      nest, nest on the branch, branch on
      the tree, tree on the hill, and the hill
      stood still.

# PUSSYCAT MOLE

Pussycat Mole
Jumped over a coal,
And in her best petticoat burnt a great hole.
Poor Pussy's weeping, she'll have no more milk,
Until her best petticoat's mended with silk.

# THE SENSES

Little eyes see pretty things,
   Little nose smells what is sweet,
Little ears hear pleasant sounds,
   Mouth likes luscious things to eat.

*Chinese Nursery Rhyme*

# LITTLE BETTY BLUE

Little Betty Blue,
        Lost her holiday shoe.
What will poor Betty do?
        Why, give her another,
To match the other,
        And then she will walk in two.

# SIX LITTLE MICE
## SAT DOWN TO SPIN

Six little mice sat down to spin,
        Pussy passed by, and she peeped in.
"What are you at, my little men?"
        "Making coats for gentlemen."
"Shall I come in and bite off your threads?"
        "No, no, Miss Pussy, you'll snip off our heads."
"Oh, no, I'll not, I'll help you to spin."
        "That may be so, but you don't come in!"

# FIVE LITTLE PIGS

1. Let us go to the wood, says this pig;
2. What to do there? says that pig;
3. To look for my mother, says this pig;
4. What to do with her? says that pig;
5. Kiss her to death, says this pig.

# THERE WERE
# TWO BLACKBIRDS

There were two blackbirds
    Sitting on a hill,
The one named Jack,
    The other named Jill.
Fly away Jack!
Fly away Jill!
Come again Jack!
Come again Jill!

143

# HERE WE GO UP, UP, UP

Here we go up, up, up,

And here we go down, down, downy;

And here we go backwards and forwards,
And here we go round, round, roundy.

# SOLOMON GRUNDY

Solomon Grundy,
Born on a Monday,
Christened on Tuesday,
Married on Wednesday,
Took ill on Thursday,
Worse on Friday,
Died on Saturday,
Buried on Sunday:
This is the end
Of Solomon Grundy.

# THIRTY DAYS
## HATH SEPTEMBER

Thirty days hath September,
       April, June, and November;
February has twenty-eight alone;
       All the rest have thirty-one,
Excepting leap-year, that's the time
       When February's days are twenty-nine.

# LITTLE ROBIN - REDBREAST

Little Robin-Redbreast sat upon a tree;
      Up went Pussy-cat, and down went he.
Down came Pussy-cat, and away Robin ran;
      Says little Robin-Redbreast, "Catch me if you
        can."
Little Robin-Redbreast jumped upon a wall;
      Pussy-cat jumped after him, and almost got a fall.
Little Robin chirped and sang, and what did Pussy say?
      Pussy-cat said "Mew," and Robin jumped away.

# SING, SING
# WHAT SHALL I SING?

Sing, sing, what shall I sing?
     The cat has eaten the pudding-string!
Do, do, what shall I do?
     The cat has bitten it quite in two.

# LADY-BUG

Lady-bug, lady-bug,
  Fly away, do,
Fly to the mountain,
  And feed upon dew,
Feed upon dew
  And sleep on a rug,
And then run away
  Like a good little bug.

*Chinese Nursery Rhyme*

149

# BLOW, WIND, BLOW!

Blow, wind, blow! And go, mill, go!
That the miller may grind his corn;
That the baker may take it,
And into rolls make it,
And send us some hot in the morn.

150

ALPHABET FUN

A was once an apple-pie,
Pidy,
Widy,
Tidy,
Pidy,
Nice insidy,
Apple-pie !

B was once a little bear,
Beary,
Wary,
Hairy,
Beary,
Taky cary,
Little bear !

C
c was once a little cake,
        Caky,
        Baky,
        Maky,
        Caky,
      Taky caky,
    Little cake!

153

D
d

was once a little doll,
Dolly,
Molly,
Polly,
Nolly,
Nursy dolly,
Little doll !

154

E
e

was once a little eel,
Eely,
Weely,
Peely,
Eely,
Twirly, tweely,
Little eel !

F
f

was once a little fish,
Fishy,
Wishy,
Squishy,
Fishy,
In a dishy,
Little fish !

# G
## g

G was once a little goose,
    Goosy,
    Moosy,
    Boosey,
    Goosey,
    Waddly-woosy,
    Little goose !

# H h

was once a little hen,
        Henny,
        Chenny,
        Tenny,
        Henny,
        Eggsy-any,
        Little  hen?

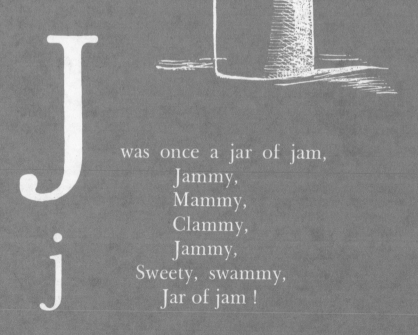

I was once a bottle of ink,
Inky,
Dinky,
Thinky,
Inky,
Blacky minky,
Bottle of ink!

J was once a jar of jam,
Jammy,
Mammy,
Clammy,
Jammy,
Sweety, swammy,
Jar of jam!

# K
### k

K was once a little kite,
  Kity,
  Whity,
  Flighty,
  Kity,
  Out of sighty,
  Little kite !

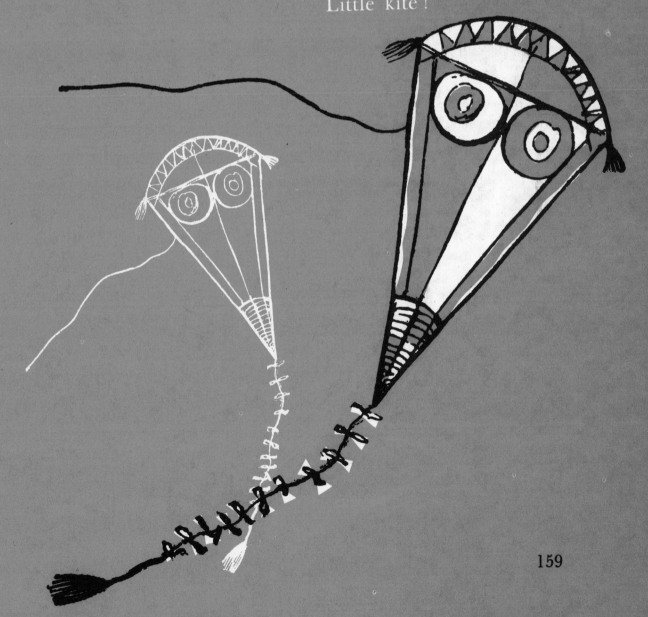

L was once a little lark,
 Larky,
 Marky,
 Harky,
 Larky,
 In the parky,
 Little lark !

# M

## m

M was once a little mouse,
Mousy,
Bousy,
Sousy,
Mousy,
In the housy,
Little mouse !

# N

## n

N was once a little needle,
Needly,
Tweedly,
Threedly,
Needly,
Wisky, Wheedly,
Little needle !

O was once a little owl,
    Owly,
    Prowly,
    Howly,
    Owly,
  Browny fowly,
  Little owl !

# P

P was once a little pump,
        Pumpy,
        Slumpy,
        Flumpy,
        Pumpy,
    Dumpy, thumpy,
    Little pump!

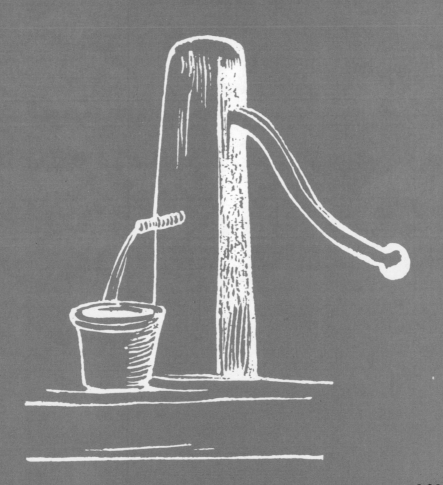

Q
q was once a little quail,
Quaily,
Faily,
Daily,
Quaily,
Stumpy-taily,
Little quail !

**R**
**r** was once a little rose,
Rosy,
Posy,
Nosy,
Rosy,
Blows-y, grows-y,
Little rose!

# S s

S was once a little shrimp,
        Shrimpy,
        Nimpy,
        Flimpy,
        Shrimpy,
    Jumpy, jimpy,
    Little shrimp !

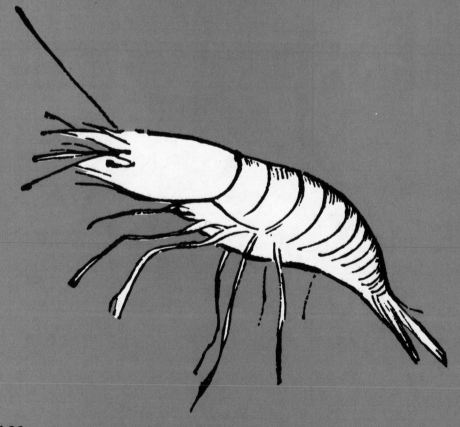

T

t was once a little thrush,
 Thrushy,
  Hushy,
  Bushy,
  Thrushy,
 Flitty, flushy,
Little thrush !

# U
u

was once a little urn,
Urny,
Burny,
Turny,
Urny,
Bubbly, burny,
Little urn !

V was once a little vine,
  Viny,
  Winy,
  Twiny,
  Viny,
  Twisty-twiny,
  Little vine !

# W

W was once a whale,
     Whaly,
      Scaly,
       Shaly,
     Whaly,
    Tumbly-taily,
   Mighty whale !

X

X was once a great king Xerxes,
Xerxy,
Perxy,
Turxy,
Xerxy,
Linxy, lurxy,
Great King Xerxes!

Y was once a little yew,
   Yewdy,
   Fewdy,
   Crudy,
   Yewdy,
Growdy, grewdy,
   Little yew !

Z was once a piece of zinc,
   Tinky,
   Winky,
   Blinky,
   Tinky,
Tinkly minky,
   Piece of zinc !

*Edward Lear*

# UPON MY WORD
# AND HONOR

As I went to Bonner,
I met a pig
Without a wig,
Upon my word and honor.

# IF ALL THE SEAS
# WERE ONE SEA

If all the seas were one sea,
       What a *great* sea that would be!
And if all the trees were one tree,
       What a *great* tree that would be!
And if all the axes were one axe,
       What a *great* axe that would be!
And if all the men were one man,
       What a *great* man he would be!
And if the *great* man took the *great* axe,
       And cut down the *great* tree,
And let it fall into the *great* sea,
       What a splish splash *that* would be!

# THERE WAS
# AN OLD MAN
# OF TOBAGO

There was an old man of Tobago,
   Who lived on rice, gruel, and sago,
Till, much to his bliss,
   His physician said this—
"To a leg, sir, of mutton you may go."

# RAIN, RAIN, GO AWAY

Rain, rain, go away;
      Come again another day;
Little [Arthur] wants to play.

# A CAT CAME FIDDLING
# OUT OF A BARN

A cat came fiddling out of a barn,
With a pair of bagpipes under her arm;
She could sing nothing but fiddle cum fee,
The mouse has married the bumble-bee.
Pipe, cat—dance, mouse,
We'll have a wedding at our good house.

177

# I AM A GOLD LOCK

(*First child.*)   1. I am a gold lock.
(*Second child.*)     2. I am a gold key
    1. I am a silver lock.
       2. I am a silver key.
    1. I am a brass lock.
       2. I am a brass key.
    1. I am a lead lock.
       2. I am a lead key.
    1. I am a monk lock.
       2. I am a monk key.

(*First child.*)    1. I went up one pair of stairs.
(*Second child.*)      2. Just like me.

            1. I went up two pair of stairs.
              2. Just like me.

            1. I went into a room.
              2. Just like me.

            1. I looked out of a window.
              2. Just like me.

            1. And there I saw a monkey.
              2. Just like me.

# THERE WAS AN OLD MAN
# AND HE HAD A CALF

There was an old man,
And he had a calf,
And that's half;

He took him out of the stall,
And put him on the wall:
And that's all.

# WHEN I WAS A BACHELOR

When I was a bachelor I lived by myself,
   And all the meat I got I put upon a shelf;
The rats and the mice did lead me such a life
   That I went to London to get myself a wife.

The streets were so broad and the lanes were so narrow,
   I could not get my wife home without a wheel-
     barrow;
The wheel-barrow broke, my wife got a fall,
   Down tumbled wheel-barrow, little wife, and all.

# TWEEDLEDUM
# AND
# TWEEDLEDEE

Tweedledum and Tweedledee
      Resolved to have a battle,
For Tweedledum said Tweedledee
      Had spoiled his nice new rattle.

Just then flew by a monstrous crow
      As big as a tar-barrel,
Which frightened both the heroes so
      They quite forgot their quarrel.

# RUB A DUB DUB

Rub a dub dub,
Three men in a tub:
And who do you think they be?
The butcher, the baker,
The candlestick-maker;
Turn 'em out, knaves all three!

183

# TAFFY
# WAS A
# WELSHMAN

Taffy was a Welshman, Taffy was a thief;
    Taffy came to my house and stole a piece of beef:
I went to Taffy's house, Taffy was not at home;
    Taffy came to my house and stole a marrow-bone.

I went to Taffy's house, Taffy was not in;
Taffy came to my house and stole a silver pin:
I went to Taffy's house, Taffy was in bed,
I took up a poker and flung it at his head.

# A STAR

I have a little sister, they call her Peep, Peep;
　　　She wades the waters deep, deep, deep;
She climbs the mountains high, high, high;
　　　Poor little creature, she has but one eye.

# A CHIMNEY

Black within and red without;
Four corners round about.

# SEE A PIN AND PICK IT UP

See a pin and pick it up,
    All the day you'll have good luck;

See a pin and let it lay,
    Bad luck you'll have all the day!

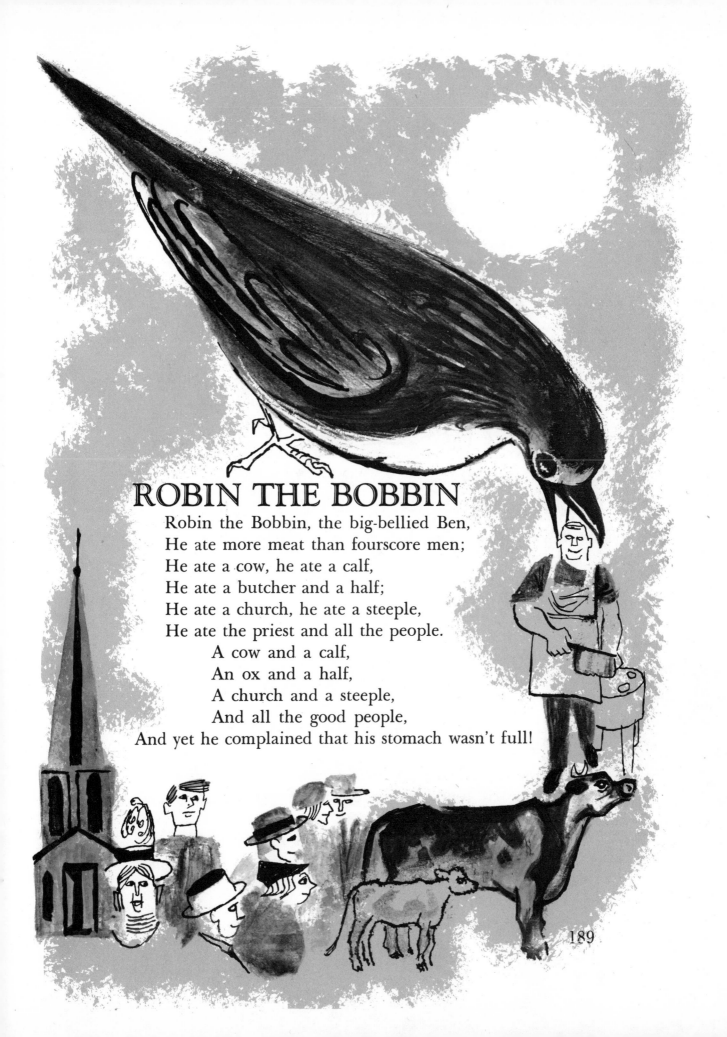

# ROBIN THE BOBBIN

Robin the Bobbin, the big-bellied Ben,
He ate more meat than fourscore men;
He ate a cow, he ate a calf,
He ate a butcher and a half;
He ate a church, he ate a steeple,
He ate the priest and all the people.
  A cow and a calf,
  An ox and a half,
  A church and a steeple,
  And all the good people,
And yet he complained that his stomach wasn't full!

189

# THERE WAS
# A CROOKED MAN

There was a crooked man, and he went a crooked mile;
    He found a crooked sixpence against a crooked
        stile:
He bought a crooked cat, which caught a crooked mouse,
    And they all lived together in a little crooked
        house.

# DANCE, LITTLE BABY
# DANCE UP HIGH

Dance, little baby, dance up high,
      Never mind, baby, mother is by;
Crow and caper, caper and crow,
      There, little baby, there you go;

Up to the ceiling, down to the ground,
      Backwards and forwards, round and round;
Dance, little baby, and mother will sing,
      With the merry chorus, ding, ding, ding!

# TWO KEYS

Hearts, like doors, will ope with ease
　　　To very, very little keys,
And don't forget that two of these,
　　　Are "I thank you" and "If you please."

# WHAT ARE LITTLE BOYS MADE OF?

What are little boys made of, made of?
      What are little boys made of?
"Snaps and snails, and puppy-dogs' tails;
      And that's what little boys are made of, made of."

What are little girls made of, made of, made of?
      What are little girls made of?
"Sugar and spice, and all that's nice;
      And that's what little girls are made of, made of."

# I HAD A LITTLE DOGGY

I had a little doggy that used to sit and beg;
       But Doggy tumbled down the stairs and broke
          his little leg.
Oh! Doggy, I will nurse you, and try to make you well,
       And you shall have a collar with a little silver
          bell.

Ah! Doggy, don't you think you should very faithful be,
       For having such a loving friend to comfort you
          as me?
And when your leg is better, and you can run and play,
       We'll have a scamper in the fields and see them
          making hay.

But, Doggy, you must promise (and mind your word you
       keep)
       Not once to tease the little lambs, or run among
          the sheep;
And then the little yellow chicks that play upon the grass,
       You must not even wag your tail to scare them
          as you pass.

# GREAT A, LITTLE A

Great A, little a,
  Bouncing B!
The cat's in the cupboard,
  And can't see me.

# FOR WANT OF A NAIL
# THE SHOE WAS LOST

For want of a nail, the shoe was lost;
      For want of the shoe, the horse was lost;
For want of the horse, the rider was lost;
      For want of the rider, the battle was lost;
For want of the battle, the kingdom was lost;
      And all for the want of a horseshoe nail.

196

# THERE WAS AN OLD WOMAN AND WHAT DO YOU THINK?

There was an old woman, and what do you think?
  She lived upon nothing but victuals and drink.
Victuals and drink were the chief of her diet;
  This tiresome old woman could never be quiet.

# I LOVE SIXPENCE
# PRETTY LITTLE SIXPENCE

I love sixpence, pretty little sixpence,
  I love sixpence better than my life;
I spent a penny of it, I spent another,
  And I took fourpence home to my wife.

O, my little fourpence, pretty little fourpence,
  I love fourpence better than my life;
I spent a penny of it, I spent another,
  And I took twopence home to my wife.

198

O, my little twopence, my pretty little twopence,
I love twopence better than my life;
I spent a penny of it, I spent another,
And I took nothing home to my wife.

O, my little nothing, my pretty little nothing,
What will nothing buy for my wife?
I have nothing, I spend nothing,
I love nothing better than my wife.

# BOUNCE BUCKRAM

Bounce buckram, velvet's dear;
Christmas comes but once a year.

200

# AS TOMMY SNOOKS
## AND BESSY BROOKS
### WERE WALKING OUT
#### ONE SUNDAY

As Tommy Snooks and Bessy Brooks
Were walking out one Sunday,
Says Tommy Snooks to Bessy Brooks,
"Tomorrow will be Monday."

201

# MOTHER, MAY I
# GO IN TO SWIM?

Mother, may I go in to swim?
     Yes, my darling daughter,
Hang your clothes on yonder tree
     But don't go near the water.

# THERE WAS AN OLD WOMAN
# LIVED UNDER A HILL

There was an old woman
            Lived under a hill,
And if she's not gone
            She lives there still.

# NEEDLES AND PINS

Needles and pins,

needles and pins,

When a man marries

his trouble begins.

# FIDDLE-DE-DEE

## FIDDLE-DE-DEE

Fiddle-de-dee, fiddle-de-dee,
　　　The fly shall marry the humble-bee.
They went to the church, and married was she:
　　　The fly has married the humble-bee.

# JENNY WREN FELL SICK

Jenny Wren fell sick,
    Upon a merry time;
In came Robin-Redbreast
    And brought her sops and wine.

"Eat well of the sops, Jenny,
    Drink well of the wine."
"Thank you, Robin, kindly,
    You shall be mine."

Jenny she got well,
　And stood upon her feet,
And told Robin plainly
　She loved him not a bit.

Robin, being angry,
　Hopped upon a twig,
Saying, "Out upon you, fie upon you,
　Bold-faced jig."

# HARK! HARK!
# THE DOGS BARK

Hark! hark! the dogs bark,
      The beggars are coming to town;
Some in rags and some in tags,
      And some in a silken gown.
Some gave them white bread,
      And some gave them brown,
And some gave them a good horse-whip,
      And sent them out of the town.

# THERE WERE THREE JOVIAL HUNTSMEN

There were three jovial huntsmen,
As I have heard them say,
And they would go a-hunting
Upon St. David's Day.

All the day they hunted,
   And nothing could they find
But a ship a-sailing,
   A-sailing with the wind.

One said it was a ship;
　The other he said nay;
The third said it was a house,
　With the chimney blown away.

And all the night they hunted,
　And nothing could they find
But the moon a-gliding,
　A-gliding with the wind.

One said it was the moon;
The other he said nay;
The third said it was a cheese,
And half o't cut away.

And all the day they hunted,
  And nothing could they find
But a hedgehog in a bramble-bush,
  And that they left behind.

The first said it was a pig;
  The second he said nay;
The third it was a pin-cushion,
  And the pins stuck in wrong way.

And all the night they hunted,
  And nothing could they find
But a hare in a turnip field,
  And that they left behind.

The first said it was a hare;
  The second he said nay;
The third said it was a calf,
  And the cow had run away.

And all the day they hunted,
  And nothing could they find
But an owl in a holly-tree,
  And that they left behind.

One said it was an owl;
  The other he said nay;
The third said 'twas an old man,
  And his beard growing grey.

# MONDAY'S CHILD
# IS FAIR OF FACE

Monday's child is fair of face;
      Tuesday's child is full of grace;
Wednesday's child is full of woe;
      Thursday's child has far to go;
Friday's child is loving and giving;
      Saturday's child works hard for its living;
But the child that is born on the Sabbath day
      Is bonny and blithe and good and gay.

215

# WHEN GOOD
# KING ARTHUR
# RULED THIS LAND

When good King Arthur ruled this land,
He was a goodly king;
He stole three pecks of barley-meal,
To make a bag-pudding.

A bag-pudding the king did make,
    And stuffed it well with plums.
And in it put great lumps of fat,
    As big as my two thumbs.

The king and queen did eat thereof,
    And noblemen beside;
And what they could not eat that night,
    The queen next morning fried.

L.L.B.

# WHERE ARE YOU GOING MY PRETTY MAID?

"Where are you going, my pretty maid?"
"I'm going a-milking, sir," she said.
"May I go with you, my pretty maid?"
"You're kindly welcome, sir," she said.
"What is your father, my pretty maid?"
"My father's a farmer, sir," she said.

"Say, will you marry me, my pretty maid?"

"Yes, if you please, kind sir," she said.

"What is your fortune, my pretty maid?"

"My face is my fortune, sir," she said.

"Then I can't marry you, my pretty maid!"

"Nobody asked you, sir," she said.

# A FARMER WENT TROTTING

A farmer went trotting
  Upon his grey mare;
Bumpety, bumpety, bump!
With his daughter behind him,
  So rosy and fair;
Lumpety, lumpety, lump!

A raven cried "Croak"
　And they all tumbled down;
Bumpety, bumpety, bump!
The mare broke her knees,
　And the farmer his crown;
Lumpety, lumpety, lump.

The mischievous raven
　Flew laughing away;
Bumpety, bumpety, bump!
And vowed he would serve them
　The same the next day;
Bumpety, bumpety, bump!

# THE OLD WOMAN

There was an old woman,
        As I have heard tell,
She went to sell pie,
        But her pie would not sell.

She hurried back home,
        But her door-step was high,
And she stumbled and fell
        And a dog ate her pie.

*Chinese Nursery Rhyme*

# THISTLE-SEED

Thistle-seed, thistle-seed,
     Fly away, fly,
The hair on your body
     Will take you up high;
Let the wind whirl you
     Around and around,
You'll not hurt yourself
     When you fall to the ground.

*Chinese Nursery Rhyme*

# TO MARKET, TO MARKET

To market, to market,
To buy a plum bun;
Home again, come again,
Market is done.

# A LITTLE COCK-SPARROW

A little cock-sparrow sat on a green tree,
And he cherruped, he cherruped, so merry was he;
A little cock-sparrow sat on a green tree,
And he cherruped, he cherruped, so merry was he.

A naughty boy came with his wee bow and arrow,
Determined to shoot this little cock-sparrow;
A naughty boy came with his wee bow and arrow,
Determined to shoot this little cock-sparrow.

"This little cock-sparrow shall make me a stew,
And his giblets shall make me a little pie too."
"Oh, no," said the sparrow, "I won't make a stew."
So he flapped his wings, and away he flew.

# BROW BENDER

Brow bender,
Eye peeper,
Nose smeller,
Mouth eater,
Chin chopper.
Knock at the door—peep in,
Lift up the latch—walk in.

Eye winker,
Tom Tinker,
Nose smeller,
Mouth eater,
Chin chopper.
Chin chopper.

226

# IF A PIG
# WORE A WIG

If a pig wore a wig,
   What could we say?
Treat him as a gentleman,
   And say "Good day."

If his tail chanced to fail,
   What could we do?—
Send him to the tailoress
   To get one new.

# THE MAN
# IN THE WILDERNESS
## ASKED ME

The man in the wilderness asked me
How many strawberries grew in the sea.
I answered him as I thought good,
As many as red herrings grew in the wood.

# UPON A GREAT
# BLACK HORSE-ILY

Upon a great black horse-ily
      A man came riding cross-ily;
A lady out did come-ily,
      Said she, "No one's at home-ily,

"But only little people-y,
      Who've gone to bed to sleep-ily."
The rider on his horse-ily
      Said to the lady, cross-ily,

"But are they bad or good-ily?
      I want it understood-ily."
"Oh, they act bad and bold-ily,
      And don't do what they're told-ily."

"Good-by!" said he, "dear Ma'am-ily,
      I've nothing for your family."
And scampered off like mouse-ily
      Away, way from the house-ily.

# MULTIPLICATION
# IS VEXATION

Multiplication is vexation,
    Division is as bad;
The Rule of Three doth puzzle me,
    And Practice drives me mad.

# ELIZABETH

Elizabeth, Elspeth, Betsy, and Bess,
They all went together to seek a bird's nest.
They found a bird's nest with five eggs in,
They all took one, and left four in.

# ALPHABET RHYMES

**A** was an Archer, and shot at a frog,
**B** was a Butcher, and had a great dog.
**C** was a Captain, all covered with lace,
**D** was a Drunkard, and had a red face.
**E** was an Esquire, with pride on his brow,
**F** was a Farmer, and followed the plough.
**G** was a Gamester, who had but ill luck,
**H** was a Hunter, and hunted a buck.
**I** was an Innkeeper, who loved to bouse,

**J** was a Joiner, and built up a house.
**K** was King William, once governed this land,
**L** was a Lady, who had a white hand.
**M** was a Miser, and hoarded up gold,
**N** was a Nobleman, gallant and bold.
**O** was an Oyster Wench, and went about town,
**P** was a Parson, and wore a black gown.
**Q** was a Queen, who was fond of good flip,
**R** was a Robber, and wanted a whip.
**S** was a Sailor, and spent all he got,
**T** was a Tinker, and mended a pot.
**U** was a Usurer, a miserable elf,
**V** was a Vintner, who drank all himself.

**W** was a Watchman, and guarded the door,
**X** was expensive, and so became poor.
**Y** was a Youth, that did not love school,
**Z** was a Zany, a poor harmless fool.

# CECILY PARSLEY

Cecily Parsley lived in a pen,
And brewed good ale for gentlemen;
Gentlemen came every day,
Till Cecily Parsley ran away.

234

CRADLE
SONGS

# WHEN
# LITTLE BIRDIE
# BYE-BYE GOES

When little Birdie bye-bye goes,
  Quiet as mice in churches,
He puts his head where no-one knows,
  On one leg he perches.

When little Babie bye-bye goes,
  On Mother's arm reposing,
Soon he lies beneath the clothes,
  Safe in the cradle dozing.

When pretty Pussy goes to sleep,
  Tail and nose together,
Then little mice around her creep,
  Lightly as a feather.

When little Babie goes to sleep,
  And he is very near us,
Then on tip-toe softly creep,
  That Babie may not hear us.
Lullaby! Lullaby! Lulla, Lulla, Lullaby!

# GOOD-NIGHT

Baby, baby, lay your head
On your pretty cradle bed;
Shut your eye-peeps, now the day
And the light are gone away;
All the clothes are tuck'd in tight;
Little baby, dear, good night.

Yes, my darling, well I know
How the bitter wind doth blow;
And the winter's snow and rain

Patter on the window-pane;
But they cannot come in here,
To my little baby dear.

For the window shutteth fast,
Till the stormy night is past,
And the curtains warm are spread
Roundabout her cradle bed;
So till morning shineth bright,
Little baby, dear, good night.

*Jane Taylor*

# MY DEAREST BABY,
# GO TO SLEEP

My dearest baby, go to sleep,
For now the bright round moon doth peep
On thy little snow-white bed,
And upon thy pretty head.

The silver stars are shining bright,
And bid my baby dear good-night;
And every bird has gone to rest
Long since in its little nest.

The lambs no longer run and leap,
But by the daisies lie asleep;
The flowers have closed their pretty eyes
Until the sun again shall rise.

All things are wrapp'd in sweet repose,
The dew falls noiseless on the rose;
So thou must like an angel lie
Till golden morning streaks the sky.

Soon will I gently steal to bed,
And rest beside thy pretty head,
And all night keep thee snug and warm,
Nestling fondly on my arm.

Then, dearest baby, go to sleep,
While the moon doth on thee peep,
Shining on thy little bed,
And around thy pretty head.

*Thomas Miller*

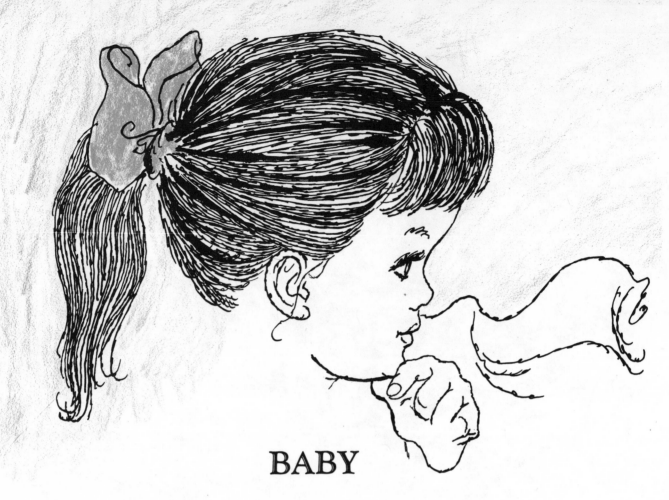

# BABY

Where did you come from, baby dear?
       Out of the everywhere into the here.

Where did you get those eyes so blue?
       Out of the sky as I came through.

What makes the light in them sparkle and spin?
       Some of the starry spikes left in.

Where did you get that little tear?
       I found it waiting when I got here.

What makes your forehead so smooth and high?
       A soft hand stroked it as I went by.

What makes your cheek like a warm white rose?
       I saw something better than anyone knows.

242

Whence that three-cornered smile of bliss?
       Three angels gave me at once a kiss.

Where did you get this pearly ear?
       God spoke, and it came out to hear.

Where did you get those arms and hands?
       Love made itself into bonds and bands.

Feet, whence did you come, you darling things?
       From the same box as the cherubs' wings.

How did they all just come to be you?
       God thought about me, and so I grew.

But how did you come to us, you dear?
       God thought about you, and so I am here.

*George Macdonald*

# THE SLEEPY SONG

As soon as the fire burns red and low
  And the house upstairs is still,
She sings me a queer little sleepy song,
  Of sheep that go over the hill.

The good little sheep run quick and soft,
  Their colors are gray and white;
They follow their leader nose and tail,
  For they must be home by night.

And one slips over, and one comes next,
  And one runs after behind;
The gray one's nose at the white one's tail,
  The top of the hill they find.

244

And when they get to the top of the hill
   They quietly slip away,
But one runs over and one comes next
   Their colors are white and gray.

And over they go, and over they go,
   And over the top of the hill
The good little sheep run quick and soft,
   And the house upstairs is still.

And one slips over and one comes next,
   The good little, gray little sheep!
I watch how the fire burns red and low,
   And she says that I fall asleep.

*Josephine Daskam Bacon*

# INFANT JOY

I have no name,
I am but two days old.
What shall I call thee?
I happy am,
Joy is my name—
Sweet joy befall thee.

Pretty joy!
Sweet joy but two days old;
Sweet joy I call thee.
Thou dost smile,
I sing the while,
Sweet joy befall thee!

*William Blake*

# LULLABY

Golden slumbers kiss your eyes,
     Smiles awake you when you rise.
Sleep, pretty wantons, do not cry,
     And I will sing a lullaby.
Rock them, rock them, lullaby.

     Care is heavy, therefore sleep you,
You are care, and care must keep you.
     Sleep, pretty wantons, do not cry,
And I will sing a lullaby.
     Rock them, rock them, lullaby.

*Thomas Dekker*

# SLEEP, SLEEP,

## BEAUTY BRIGHT

Sleep, sleep, beauty bright,
Dreaming in the joys of night;
Sleep, sleep; in thy sleep
Little sorrows sit and weep.

Sweet babe, in thy face
Soft desires I can trace,
Secret joys and secret smiles,
Little pretty infant wiles.

As thy softest limbs I feel,
Smiles as of the morning steal
O'er thy cheek, and o'er thy breast
Where thy little heart doth rest.

Oh the cunning wiles that creep
In thy little heart asleep!
When thy little heart doth wake
Then the dreadful light shall break.

*William Blake*

# NIGHT

The snow is white, the wind is cold—
      The king has sent for my three-year-old.
Bring the pony and shoe him fast
      With silver shoes that were made to last.
Bring the saddle trimmed with gold;
      Put foot in stirrup, my three-year-old;
Jump in the saddle, away, away!
      And hurry back by the break of day;
By break of day, through dale and down,
      And bring me the news from Slumbertown.

*Mary F. Butts*

# LULLABY, OH, LULLABY!

Lullaby, oh, lullaby!
Flowers are closed and lambs are sleeping;
Lullaby, oh, lullaby!
Stars are up, the moon is peeping;
Lullaby, oh, lullaby!
While the birds are silence keeping,
Lullaby, oh, lullaby!
Sleep, my baby, fall a-sleeping,
Lullaby, oh, lullaby!

*Christina G. Rossetti*

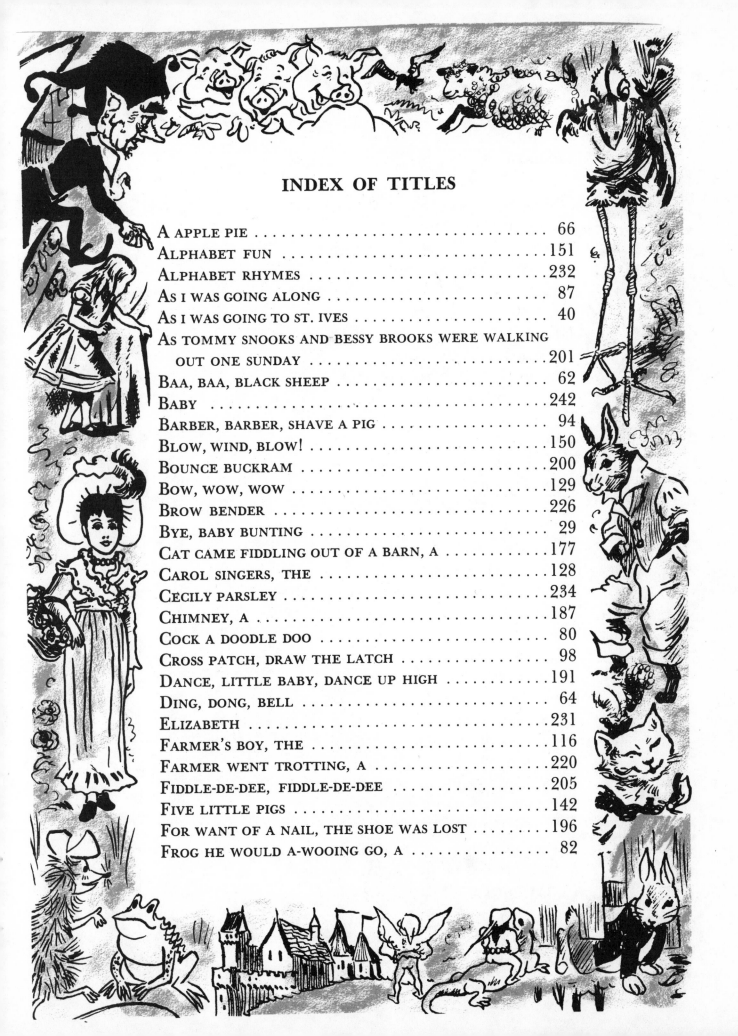

# INDEX OF TITLES